One dog and his man

Dalesman

Dalesman Publishing Company Ltd
Stable Courtyard, Broughton Hall,
Skipton, North Yorkshire BD23 3AZ

First published 1999

© Silvey-Jex Partnership

A British Library Cataloguing in Publication record
is available for this book

ISBN 1 85568 169 2

Printed by Amadeus Press, Huddersfield

SHEEP DOG TRAINING SCHOOL

BLECCHH! I THINK I'VE GOT YOURS

I DISTINCTLY SAID "HAVE WE PACKED LUNCH?" AND YOU SAID "YES"

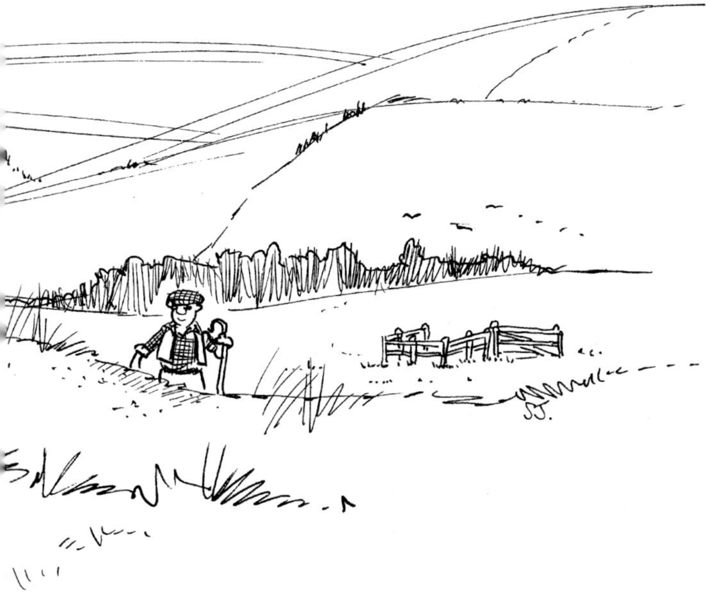
SJ.

I'M SORRY – BUT I DON'T MAKE THE RULES